CONTENTS

Preface

As a junior high mathematics teacher I am fully aware of the importance of giving students some kind of activity at the beginning of class. A *Warm-Up* activity, like those included in this book, can set the stage for the remainder of the period in addition to reviewing basic mathematical concepts. Also, a *Warm-Up* usually allows the teacher a few minutes of uninterrupted time to take care of those chores that seem to arise at the start of class.

There are not enough *Warm-Ups* to be used on a one-a-day basis. On other days, perhaps students can start with a challenge problem, some mental computation exercises, or a quiz.

Good luck with the *Warm-Up* activities. They should provide your students with some good review as well as some challenging mathematical experiences.

Scott McFadden
Eugene Public Schools
Eugene, Oregon

MATH WARM-UPS
For Jr. High

By

Scott McFadden

Editor: Geri Rothacker
Production Coordinator: Ruth Cottrell

ISBN 0-86651-107-5

Order Number DSO1330

1516 17 18 19 20-MA-00

DALE
SEYMOUR
PUBLICATIONS
P.O. BOX 10888
PALO ALTO, CA 94303

INTRODUCTION

What is *Warm-Ups for Jr. High*?

Warm-Ups for Jr. High contains 70 warm-up lessons. Each *Warm-Up* includes a set of five problems and an enrichment problem called a BONUS.

What are some special features of the *Warm-Ups?*

- Skill Maintenance — Students need frequent reviews of mathematical concepts and skills. The *Warm-Ups* provide this necessary skill maintenance and concept reinforcement.

- Concept Development — Although much of the content of the *Warm-Ups* is review, some exercises are designed to develop certain concepts. It is likely, however, that the teacher may need to provide more concept development for some topics.

- Mental Computation — Many opportunities are provided for students to practice mental computation techniques. This mental computation feature needs to be continually emphasized with students. Teachers are reminded of this in the Teacher Commentary pages.

- Problem Solving — The bonus problems are intended to provide challenging problem solving experiences for all students. Many of the bonus problems can be easily extended to further enrich these experiences.

- Teacher Commentary — Answers and some comments are provided for each *Warm-Up*. Many of the comments are intended to stimulate discussion when the problems are gone over in class.

For what level are the *Warm-Ups* intended?

- The *Warm-Ups* can be used at any junior high grade level because the topics reviewed are usually ones that appear in the upper elementary school curriculum.
  The main topics included in the *Warm-Ups* are: whole numbers, fractions, decimals, money, percent, measurement, and geometry.

- *Warm-Ups* can be used effectively with low achievers. Perhaps some of the exercises will need to be simplified and more time may be needed.
  The *Warm-Ups* can serve as an excellent diagnostic tool. The teacher can easily provide additional practice when certain weaknesses are diagnosed.

- Many high achievers in junior high also need to have frequent review of mathematical concepts. The *Warm-Ups* should provide this review. Also, the bonus problems should create a high degree of stimulation for advanced students.

1

How should the *Warm-Ups* be used?

- Enough *Warm-Ups* (70 in all) are included, so two of them can be used each week.

- The *Warm-Ups* are short. Most can be done in about 10 minutes.

- Every page contains two *Warm-Ups.* After a page is duplicated, the two *Warm-Ups* should be separated and distributed on different days.

- *Warm-Ups* should be done at the beginning of the class period. They provide a good "warm-up" to the rest of the period's activities.

- Certain topics are developed and reinforced many times throughout the book. Thus, it is best if the *Warm-Ups* are done in the order in which they appear.

- *Warm-Ups* can easily be graded on a 5-point basis with an extra credit point given for the bonus. Items similar to the *Warm-Ups* should be frequently included on quizzes and tests.

WARM-UP 2

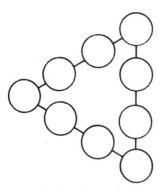

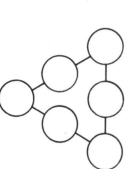

1. $17 \times (50 + 80) =$ _____
   (Remember, add the numbers inside the parentheses first.)

2. $(17 \times 50) + (17 \times 80) =$ _____
   (Remember, multiply the numbers inside the parentheses first.)

3. $29.02 - 17.03 =$ _____

4. $13 \overline{)385,385}$ _____ (You should *not* get a remainder.)

5. $205 \times 739 =$ _____

BONUS: Use each of the numbers 1 through 9. The sum of the numbers along each side must be 20.

WARM-UP 1

1. $3.98 + 12.63 + 14 =$ _____

2. $1.99 \times 15 =$ _____

3. A grocery cart contains eggs for 89¢, bread for 95¢, fruit for $1.79, meat for $2.89, and vegetables for $1.29. What is the total cost? _____

4. In problem 3, how much change will you get back, if you give the clerk $20? _____

5. Find the perimeter of this rectangle. (Remember, the perimeter is the distance around.) _____

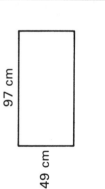

97 cm

49 cm

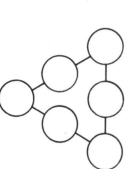

BONUS: Use each of the numbers 1 through 6. The sum of the numbers on each side must be the same. (There are four different solutions. Can you find them all?)

3

WARM-UP 4

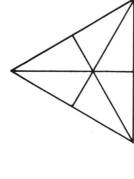

1. $79 − $79 = _____

2. Round $17.86 to the nearest

   dollar. _____

3. Round $53.19 to the nearest

   dime. _____

4. 13 ⟌ 216,216   (You should *not* get a

   remainder.)

5. Find the average of 32, 51,
   43, 39, 47, and 40.

   _____

BONUS: How many
triangles are there?

_____

WARM-UP 3

1. 7 × 8 × 10 × 8 × 0 × 25 = _____

2. Big Spender bought 5 TVs at $499
   each. What was the total cost?

   _____

3. 27 × (35 + 46) = _____

4. (27 × 35) + (27 × 46) = _____

5. Find the perimeter of this
   square. (Remember, all
   four sides are equal.)

   _____

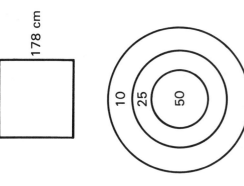

178 cm

BONUS: Use 3 darts. Each
dart must hit the board. How
many different scores are

possible? _____

4

WARM-UP 6

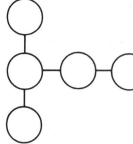

1.
$$
\begin{array}{r}
\square\ 9 \\
\times\ \square \\
\hline
3\ 1\ 5
\end{array}
$$

2. Round $6435 to the nearest hundred dollars. _____

3. Round 56,491 to the nearest thousand. _____

4. Slim bought 15 sodas at $.49 each and 15 hamburgers at $.99 each. What was the total cost? _____

5. 15 people are at a party. Mrs. Jones bought all the food. Each person had a $.49 soda and a $.99 hamburger.

   What was the total cost? _____

BONUS: Use only the numbers 1 through 5. The sum in each direction must be the same. Find 3 different sums.

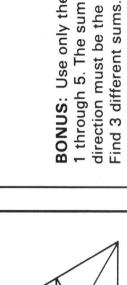

WARM-UP 5

1. Find the perimeter of this regular hexagon. (In a regular hexagon each side has the same length.) _____

29 cm

2. Find the average of $.85, $1.35, $7, $1.95, and $2.05. _____

3. $27 \times 10 \times 16 \times 0 \times 83 \times 14 + 71 =$ _____

4.
$$
\begin{array}{r}
\square\ \square\ 5 \\
+\ 3\ 8\ 5 \\
\hline
8\ 0\ 0
\end{array}
$$

5. $23.62 + $19.17 + $\square$ = $100

BONUS: How many triangles are in this figure? _____

WARM-UP 8

1. What number times itself is 144? (Your answer is called the *square root* of 144.) _____

2. What is the square root of 289? _____

3.
```
  ☐ ☐ ☐
1 0 0 0
- ☐ ☐ ☐
  3 3 3
```

4. 289,289 ÷ 11 = _____ (You should *not* get a remainder.)

5. Is there a 4th of July in England? _____

BONUS: Old McDonald raises ducks and cows. The animals have a total of 32 heads and 72 feet. How many ducks and how many cows does Mr. McDonald have? _____

WARM-UP 7

1. What is one less than one million? _____

2. Add. Look for shortcuts.
   95 + 88 + 5 + 25 + 12 + 410 + 75 + 8 = _____

3. Find the average of the bowling scores 135, 185, 160, and 148. _____

4. Complete the table showing the cost of pens at $.85 each.

Number	1	2	4	8	16
Cost $	.85				

5. This is 1 centimeter: _____
   Estimate the length of segment *AB* in centimeters. _____

   A ——————————— B

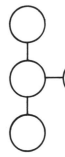

BONUS: Use only the numbers 20 through 24. The sum in each direction must be the same. Find three different sums.

WARM-UP 9

1. $20{,}010 \div 27 =$ _____ (If the problem is done correctly, the remainder is 3.)

2. Add. Look for shortcuts.
   $89 + 70 + 15 + 30 + 11 + 85 + 49 =$ _____

3. Find the square root of 625. _____

4. Estimate the length of segment CD in centimeters. _____

   C _____ D

5. A millimeter is one-tenth of a centimeter. Estimate the length of segment CD in millimeters.

   _____

BONUS: Old McDonald raises goats and chickens. The animals have a total of 100 heads and 360 feet. How many goats and how many chickens does Mr. McDonald have?

WARM-UP 10

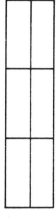

1. What is one less than one billion?

   _____

2. Complete the table showing the cost of ice cream bars at 45¢ each.

Number	1	2	3	4	8	16
Cost $	.45					

Complete the following patterns.

3. 1, 2, 4, 8, 16, 32, ____, ____, ____

4. 2, 10, 18, 26, 34, ____, ____, ____

5. 1, 3, 6, 10, 15, ____, ____, ____

BONUS: How many rectangles are there?

WARM-UP 12

1. Use each of the numbers 4, 5, 6, and 7 in the boxes. Find the largest answer.

2. $3.27 + $.79 + $2.35 + $17 + $10.43 = _____

3. 52)‾28,142

4. Find the area of the rectangle in square inches. (Remember, the area is the number of square inches "inside".) _____

18 in.

13 in.

5. Find the area of the rectangle in square centimeters. _____

53 cm

17 cm

BONUS: Use each of the numbers 1 through 9. The sum of the numbers along each side must be 17.

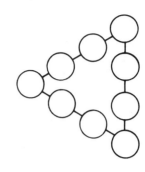

WARM-UP 11

1. Estimate segment EF in
   a) centimeters _____
   b) millimeters _____

   E _____ F

2. Complete each pattern:
   a) 73, 65, 57, 49, ____, ____, ____
   b) 2, 5, 9, 14, 20, ____, ____, ____

3. 15 + 5 × 10 = _____ (The answer is *not* 200.)

4.
```
    9 , 9   9   9
  +   ☐   ☐   ☐
  ─────────────
    1   2   3   4   5
```

5. 7)‾768,768 _____ (You should *not* get a remainder.)

BONUS: How many rectangles are there? _____

8

WARM-UP 13

1. ($2.67 + $15.93) − ($1.15 + $8.98) = _____

2. 15 pens at $.79 each
   13 erasers at $.29 each

   Total Cost _____

3. Find the perimeter (distance around) of this rectangle. _____

35 cm

15 cm

4. Find the area (amount "inside") of the above figure. _____

5. 23 + 7 × 16 = _____

BONUS: Use each of the numbers 1, 2, 3, 4, 6, 7, 8, and 9. Make a magic square. The magic sum in each direction and diagonally, must be 15.

	5	

9

WARM-UP 14

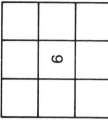

1. Multiply each number by 1000.

   a) 234 _____   b) 1000 _____

   c) 98,765 _____

2. P = A + B + C

   Find P if A = 23
             B = 17
             C = 29

   P = _____

3. P = 2 × (L + W)

   Find P if L is 83 and W is 17.

   P = _____

4. Round $149.99 to the

   a) nearest dime _____

   b) nearest 100 dollars _____

5. 217,217 ÷ 11 = _____
   (You should *not* get a remainder.)

BONUS: Complete this magic square. Use each of the numbers 2, 3, 4, 5, 7, 8, 9, and 10. The magic sum is 18.

	6	

WARM-UP 16

1. Add all the whole numbers 1 through 20. _____

2. Multiply 56 by
   a) 10 _____
   b) 100 _____
   c) 1000 _____

3. Find the volume of this rectangular solid. (Remember, the volume is the number of cubic inches "inside.")

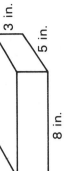

8 in. 3 in. 5 in.

_____

4. Find the volume of this rectangular solid.

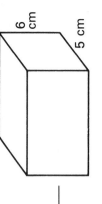

6 cm 10 cm 5 cm

_____

5. Complete the pattern:
   1, 4, 9, 16, 25, 36, ___, ___, ___, ___, ___

BONUS:

Study this pattern:
2, 3, 5, 8, 13, 21, 34

Notice that $2 + 3 = 5$
$3 + 5 = 8$
$5 + 8 = 13$

This is called the Adding Pattern.
Complete these patterns:

a) 7, 8, 15, ___, ___, ___, ___, ___

b) 6, ___, 9, ___, ___, ___, ___, ___

c) 2, ___, ___, ___, 34, ___

WARM-UP 15

1. $123.17 - $99.99 = _____

2. What is one less than one trillion? _____

3. These amounts were charged on Mr. Moneybags's charge card: $5.49, $112.63, $15.85, $6.73, $99.99, and $251.50. What was the total amount charged? _____

4. $P = 2 \times (L + W)$
   Find P if L is 29 and W is 23.

   $P = $ _____

5. $P = 2 \times L + 2 \times W$
   Find P if L is 29 and W is 23.

   $P = $ _____

BONUS:

Write a 3-digit number.
Write the same 3 digits after the number so that you have a 6-digit number; for example, 352352.
Divide the new number by 13.
Divide your answer by 11.
Divide this new answer by 7.
Comment on your result.

_____

10

WARM-UP 17

1. Add all the whole numbers 1 through 40. _____

2. Find the average of the test scores: 75, 89, 100, 75, 85, and 98. _____

3. $31.32 ÷ 27 = _____

4. 5 grapefruits cost 99¢. How much will 1 grapefruit cost? _____

5. Find the volume of this cube. (Remember, in a cube all the edges are the same.) _____

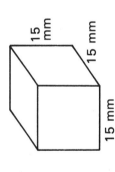

15 mm
15 mm
15 mm

BONUS:
Use the Adding Pattern to complete the following:
a) 10, 3, 13, 16, ____, ____, ____, ____, ____, ____
b) 1, ____, ____, ____, 14, ____, ____, ____, 97

Make up one of your own. Give it to a classmate to solve.

WARM-UP 18

1. 5^3 means $5 \times 5 \times 5$. Find 5^3. _____

2. Find 6^3. _____

3. Dan bought a book for $6.29. How much change did he get from $10. _____

4. A farmer had 17 sheep. All but 9 died. How many does he have left? _____

5. $988 + 297 + 12 + 550 + 3 =$ _____

BONUS:
Use the Adding Pattern to complete the following:
a) 5, 12, 17, 29, ____, ____, ____, ____, 29, 47
b) ____, ____, ____, ____, ____, ____, ____
c) 3, ____, ____, 10, ____, ____

WARM-UP 19

1. Add all the whole numbers 1 through 100. _____

2. Find 9^3. (The answer is *not* 27.) _____

3. The total cost of a picnic is $38.75. The cost is divided equally among 25 people. How much should each person pay? _____

4.
```
    □ □ □
    3 7 5
  + 6 1 9
  -------
  1 6 0 4
```

5.
```
    7 8 1 3
  -   □ □ □ □
  -----------
    2 9 0 5
```

⑤ 11 ⑥
  19 20
  ⑭

BONUS: Notice that the numbers in the circles have been added to give the numbers in between.

What numbers should be put in these circles?

a) 14 16 — with circle 12

b) 15 22 — with circle 11

c) 57 60 — with circle 35

WARM-UP 20

1. Find the square root of 256. (What number times itself is 256?) _____

2. Big Spender bought 12 stereo sets for $299 each. What was the total cost? _____

3. $99 – $.99 = _____

4. Round $185.93 to the
   a) nearest $10 _____
   b) nearest $1 _____

5. How much dirt is in a hole 2 feet by 3 feet by 4 feet? _____

BONUS: The numbers that belong in the circles can be added to give the numbers in between. What numbers belong in the circles?

a) 37 50 — with circle 27

b) 31 44 — with circle 17

c) 14 12 — with circle 19

WARM-UP 21

1. How much larger is 2^5 than 5^2? _____

2. One dollar is divided equally among 7 boys. About how much should each boy receive? _____

3. $8320 \div 54 =$ _____

4. $2.83 + $7.61 + $9.84 + $6 =$ _____

5. $5.64 + 2.93 + 4.86 + 7 =$ _____

BONUS: How many triangles are in this figure? _____

WARM-UP 22

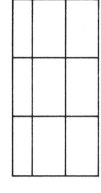

1. Shade approximately $\frac{1}{5}$ of this rectangle.

2. Shade approximately $\frac{3}{4}$ of this rectangle.

3. $1 - $.59 =$ _____

4. Regular price — $.98 each. Sale price — 3 for $2.49. How much is saved if one item is purchased on sale? _____

5.
```
      3  9 R 1
   8 | ☐ ☐ ☐
```

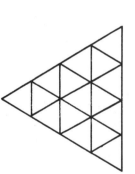

BONUS: How many rectangles are there? (Remember, a square is a rectangle.) _____

13

WARM-UP 23

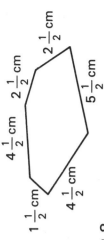

1. $215.73 − $199.98 = _____

2. 516.43 − 289.66 = _____

3. Shade approximately $\frac{2}{4}$ of the rectangle.

4. Shade approximately $\frac{4}{8}$ of the rectangle.

5. Write 8 fractions that are equivalent to $\frac{1}{2}$. _____

BONUS: Use four 4s and any of the four operations to make all the numbers from 1 through 10.

Example: $3 = (4 + 4 + 4) \div 4$

WARM-UP 24

1. Find the perimeter of this hexagon. _____

2. 13) 9 1 R 8
□□□□

3. Write all the whole number divisors of 48. _____

4. a) How many dimes are in $7.40? _____
   b) How many pennies are in $7.40? _____

5. a) $7.40 × 10 = _____
   b) $7.40 × 100 = _____

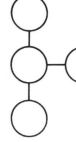

BONUS: Use only the odd numbers 1, 3, 5, 7, 9, 11. The sum in each direction must be the same.

WARM-UP 25

1. A pizza is cut into 6 equal parts. Show how this can be done. What fraction of the pizza is

   each part? _____

2. 3.84 + .72 + 6.94 + 8 = _____

3. $17 − $1.79 = _____

4. 15 − 3.62 = _____

5. Shade .9 of the rectangle.

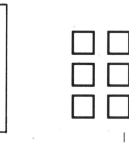

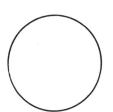

BONUS: Use the digits 2 through 7. Make the smallest answer you can. The smallest answer is less than 50.

WARM-UP 26

1. Write 4 fractions that are

   equivalent to $\frac{1}{3}$. _____

   _____

2. Multiply.

   a) 3.24 × 10 _____

   b) 3.24 × 100 _____

   c) 3.24 × 1000 _____

3. Find the perimeter of this rectangle. _____

   5.5 cm

   1.5 cm

4. Approximately how long and how wide is this paper in

   centimeters? _____

5. Gene agrees to pay $\frac{2}{3}$ of the cost of a $7.50 pizza. How much

   should he pay? _____

BONUS: Replace each star with a number 0 through 9. You cannot use a number more than once. How many solutions can you find?

15

WARM-UP 28

1. Use the number line.
   Give the approximate location
   of each of these decimals:
   .5, .1, .9.

   0 ——————————— 1

2. Write three decimals that are
   between .1 and .5.

   _____

3. $P = A + B + C$
   Find P if $A = 18\frac{1}{2}$
   $B = 10\frac{1}{2}$
   $C = 19$

   $P =$ _____

4. $P = 2 \times (L + W)$
   Find P if $L = 16.5$
   $W = 13.5$

   $P =$ _____

5. Arthur has two U.S. coins totalling
   55 cents. One is not a nickel. What
   coins does Arthur have?

   _____

BONUS: How many ways can
you make change for 25¢? You
can use pennies, nickels, and

dimes. _____

WARM-UP 27

1. $15.96 + \boxed{} = 18.04$

2. a) $\$37.95 - \$19 =$ _____

   b) $42.63 - 26 =$ _____

3. Use the number line. Show the
   approximate location of each of
   these fractions: $\frac{1}{2}$, $\frac{1}{4}$, $\frac{9}{10}$.

   0 ——————————— 1

4. Write a fraction that is between
   $\frac{1}{4}$ and $\frac{1}{2}$.

   _____

5. $19^2 =$ _____

BONUS: Use only the numbers at the
right to make an answer of 1. You
can use any operations you like.
Find as many ways as you can.

Here's one possibility: 1, 7, 6, 22, 6

$(22 - 7) \times (6 - 6) + 1 = 1$

WARM-UP 30

1. Write 3 decimals that are between .3 and .4

   _____

2. Write 3 fractions that are between $\frac{1}{2}$ and 1.

   _____

3. Approximately what is the area of this rectangle in square centimeters?

   _____

4. Write all the whole number divisors of
   a) 36   b) 53

   _____

5. A pen costs $1 more than a pencil. Together they cost $1.10. What is the cost of the pencil?

   _____

BONUS:
a) What 6 coins have a value of 48¢?

   _____

b) What 14 coins have a value of 48¢?

   _____

WARM-UP 29

1. $8 \times (\$3.74 + \$2.84) =$ _____

2. $(8 \times \$3.74) + (8 \times \$2.84) =$ _____

3. Complete the pattern.

   $\frac{1}{4}$, $\frac{1}{2}$, $\frac{3}{4}$, ___, ___, ___

4. Complete the pattern.

   .25, .50, .75, ___, ___, ___

5. Circle all the numbers that are the same.

   $\frac{1}{2}$, .5, $\frac{5}{10}$, 5, .05, .50

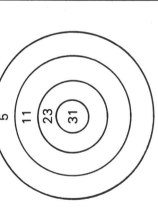

5
11
23
31

BONUS: Show how to score 74 with 6 darts. All six darts must hit the board.

17

WARM-UP 32

1. Arrange from smallest to largest.

   $\dfrac{1}{4}$, $\dfrac{1}{100}$, $\dfrac{9}{10}$, $\dfrac{1}{2}$ _____

2. Arrange from smallest to largest.

   .5, .01, .9, .25 _____

3. Find the perimeter.

   _____

$6\dfrac{1}{2}$ cm

2.5 cm

4. a) $9 \times \$7.96 =$ _____

   b) $8 \times 5.43 =$ _____

5. If possible, write the greatest fraction less than 1. _____

BONUS: A man gave 4 cents each to some children. Had he given them 7 cents each, it would have taken 36 cents more. How many children were there?

_____

WARM-UP 31

1. Add. Look for shortcuts.

   $1\dfrac{9}{10} + 5\dfrac{1}{2} + \dfrac{1}{10} + 10 + 5\dfrac{1}{2} =$ _____

2. $1.9 + 5.5 + .1 + 10 + 5.5 =$ _____

3. Complete the pattern

   $\dfrac{3}{8}$, $\dfrac{5}{8}$, $\dfrac{7}{8}$, $1\dfrac{1}{8}$, _____, _____, _____

4. Round $345.67 to the

   a) nearest $10 _____

   b) nearest $1 _____

   c) nearest dime (tenth of a dollar)

   _____

5. Round 529.48 to the

   a) nearest tens _____

   b) nearest units _____

   c) nearest tenth _____

BONUS: Use pennies, nickels, dimes and quarters. How many ways can you make change

for 30¢? _____

18

WARM-UP 33

1. Round to the indicated position.

   a) 31.412 (nearest hundredth) _____

   b) 415.91 (nearest unit) _____

   c) 93.64 (nearest hundred) _____

2. Find the perimeter of this square.

   15.5 cm

   a) Show how to get the answer by adding. _____

   b) Show how to get the answer by multiplying. _____

3. Find the perimeter of a square that is $30\frac{1}{2}$ inches on a side. _____

4. Jill bought a TV for $395.99. How much less than $400 is this? _____

5. Write 11 thousand 11 hundred eleven. (Be careful!) _____

BONUS: How many squares are in this figure? (There are more than 16.)

WARM-UP 34

1. Write 4 fractions that are equivalent to $\frac{2}{3}$. _____

2. Write 4 fractions that are equivalent to $\frac{1}{4}$. _____

3. Write 4 fractions between $\frac{1}{4}$ and $\frac{2}{3}$. _____

4. $\frac{2}{3} + \frac{1}{4} =$ _____

5. $\frac{2}{3} - \frac{1}{4} =$ _____

BONUS:

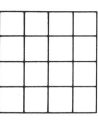

19

WARM-UP 36

1. Find the perimeter of this parallelogram.

   5 ft 7 in.   2 ft 5 in.

   _____

2. Find the length of *N*.

   2 yd 2 ft   4 yd   *N*

   _____

3. $\frac{1}{2} + \frac{1}{3} + \frac{1}{4} =$ _____

4. Write .85 as a fraction and then reduce it to lowest terms.

   _____

5. Write .48 as a fraction and then reduce it to lowest terms.

   _____

BONUS:

```
          2 □
       ┌────────
  214 )│ □ □ □ □
       │ □ □ □
       ├────────
       │   □ □ □
       │   □ □ 6
       ├────────
       │       0
```

WARM-UP 35

1. 3 hr and 75 min is the same as

   4 hr and _____ min.

2. 2 hr 20 min
   + 5 hr 40 min   (Your answer should be
   _____   in lowest terms.)

3. 2 ft 7 in.
   + 8 ft 9 in.   (Your answer should be
   _____   in lowest terms.)

4. 5 yd 1 ft
   − 2 yd 2 ft
   _____

5. 15 cm 3 mm
   − 6 cm 9 mm
   _____

BONUS: There are 8 teams in a basketball league. If each team plays every other team, how many games are played

altogether? _____

20

WARM-UP 37

1. Arrange from smallest to largest.

   $\frac{2}{3}$, .8 , .001 , $\frac{1}{4}$, .50 _____

2. Circle *all* the numbers that are the same as $\frac{4}{3}$.

   $\frac{40}{30}$, $\frac{3}{4}$, 1.3, $1\frac{1}{3}$, 1.3̄3̄, $\frac{8}{6}$

3. Circle *all* the numbers that are the same as $3\frac{1}{4}$.

   $3\frac{2}{8}$, $\frac{13}{4}$, $\frac{31}{10}$, 3.25, $2\frac{5}{4}$, $\frac{13}{3}$

4. $\frac{3}{4} + \frac{5}{6} =$ _____

5. $\frac{9}{10} - \frac{3}{5} =$ _____

BONUS: How can you pay each of these amounts with five coins?

a) 17¢ _____   b) 13¢ _____

c) 53¢ _____   d) 40¢ _____

e) 41¢ _____   f) 66¢ _____

WARM-UP 38

1.   3 yd 1 ft 3 in.
   −1 yd 2 ft 8 in.
   _____

2. Find the square root of 324. _____

3. Find the square root of 34. Give your answer to the nearest tenth. (Should your first guess be closer to 5 or 6?) _____

4. Complete the pattern.

   2.2,   1.9,   1.6,   1.3,   _____ ,   _____ ,

5. .36 + 3.6 + 36 = _____

BONUS: Billy Biceps did 1 push-up on the first of January. He did 2 push-ups on Jan. 2nd, 4 push-ups on Jan. 3rd, 8 on Jan. 4th, etc. If he continued with this plan, how many push-ups would Billy do on Jan. 16? _____ Do you think this is possible? _____

WARM-UP 40

1. Find the perimeter.

   $\frac{7}{8}''$ $1\frac{1}{2}''$ $2\frac{1}{4}''$

   _____

2. Find the area of this square.

   1.8 cm

   _____

3. The area of a square is 144 square centimeters. What is the length of a side?

   144 sq centimeters ?

   _____

4. Find the square root of 30. Give your answer to the nearest tenth.

   _____

5. Add.
   .008 + .08 + .8 + 8 + 80

   _____

BONUS: Ten people are in a room. They all shake hands with each other. What is the total number of handshakes?

   _____

WARM-UP 39

1. $1.5 - .39 =$ _____

2. $.8 + 1.37 + 6 =$ _____

3. $\frac{1}{2} + .81 + \frac{3}{4} =$ _____

4. $3.25 - 1.75 =$ _____

5. $3\frac{1}{4} - 1\frac{3}{4} =$ _____

BONUS: The average weight of four football players is 180 pounds. The weights of three of the players are 165 pounds, 185 pounds, and 215 pounds. What is the weight of the fourth player? _____

22

WARM-UP 41

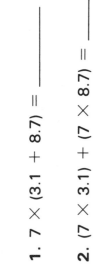

1. $7 \times (3.1 + 8.7) = $ _____

2. $(7 \times 3.1) + (7 \times 8.7) = $ _____

3. Find the perimeter of this rectangle. _____

1.8 cm

3.2 cm

4. Find the area of the above rectangle. _____

5. How many 3¢ stamps are there in a dozen? _____

BONUS: Use the numbers 4, 6, 7, 8, 10, 11, 12, 13, 14, and 15 to complete this magic square. The sum of the numbers in each row, column, and diagonal must be 34.

		9	3
	16	5	
	2		1

WARM-UP 42

1. How many nickels are in $3.65? _____

2. $.05\overline{)3.65}$

3. How many quarters are in $8.75? _____

4. $.25\overline{)8.75}$

5. How many $.85 hamburgers can Slim buy for $10? _____

BONUS:

```
        ☐  ☐  7
      × ☐  3
      _____
   ☐  ☐  0  ☐
☐  ☐  ☐  ☐
_____
☐  7 , ☐  ☐  3
```

3 5

3

WARM-UP 43

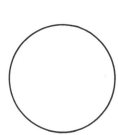

1. Find the average of 1.2, 3.8, 2.9, and 6.1. _____

2. 5 − 2.9 = _____

3. $7\frac{4}{4} - 2\frac{3}{4}$ = _____

4. $8 - 2\frac{3}{4}$ = _____

5. $11 - 1\frac{1}{8}$ = _____

BONUS: It is possible to use only 4 cuts to divide a pizza into 11 pieces. Show how this can be done. (Each cut must be straight. The pieces do not have to be the same size.)

WARM-UP 44

1. Find the average of 2.8, 2.9, 3.0, 3.1, and 3.2. _____

39 m

195 sq meters

?

2. The area of this rectangle is 195 square meters. The length is 39 meters. What is the width? _____

3. The area of a rectangle is 190 sq cm. The width is 9.5 cm. Find the length. _____

4. $1\frac{3}{4} + \boxed{} = 4$

5. $2.9 + \boxed{} = 8$

BONUS:
a) How many ways can a committee of two be selected from 5 people? _____

b) How many ways can a committee of three be selected from 5 people? _____

WARM-UP 45

1. Add. Look for shortcuts.
$5\frac{1}{8} + 2\frac{1}{2} + 6\frac{3}{4} + 2.5 + 1\frac{7}{8} + 8\frac{1}{4} +$ _____

2. $(2.3)^3 =$ _____   (The answer is *not* 6.9.)

3. $12\frac{1}{6} - 5\frac{1}{3} =$ _____

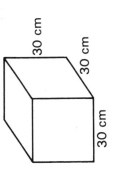

30 cm

30 cm

30 cm

4. Find the volume of this cube.
Each edge is 30 cm. _____

5. Find the volume of a cube if
each edge is 2.3 cm. _____

BONUS: If a hen and a half lays
an egg and a half in a day and a
half, how many eggs will 6 hens

lay in 6 days. _____

WARM-UP 46

1. Arrange from smallest to largest.
.7, .71, 7, .07, .17 _____

2. First make an estimate. Then solve the problem.

$2.1 \times .99 =$ _____ (Estimate)

$2.1 \times .99 =$ _____ (Solution)

3. First make an estimate. Then solve the problem.

$4.29 \times .5 =$ _____ (Estimate)

$4.29 \times .5 =$ _____ (Solution)

4. a) $5.93 \times 10 =$ _____

   b) $5.93 \times 100 =$ _____

   c) $5.93 \times 1000 =$ _____

5. a) $6490 \div 10 =$ _____

   b) $6490 \div 100 =$ _____

   c) $6490 \div 1000 =$ _____

BONUS: Use only the numbers at
the right to make an answer of 11.
You can use any operation you
like. Find as many ways as you can.
Here's one possibility:
$\frac{8+8}{2} + 13 - 10 = 11$

2, 8, 13, 10, 8

WARM-UP 48

28" 17"
9" 35"

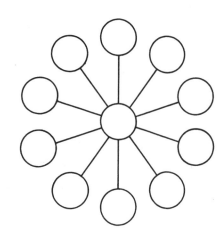

1. Find the perimeter. _____

2. $3\frac{1}{2} \times 4\frac{1}{2} =$ _____

3. Find the answer to problem 2 by using decimals. _____

4. $2\frac{1}{10} \times 5\frac{1}{10} =$ _____

5. $\begin{array}{r} 3 \text{ ft } 7 \text{ in.} \\ + 6 \text{ ft } 8 \text{ in.} \\ \hline \end{array}$

BONUS: Use only the numbers 1 through 11. The sum in each direction must be the same.

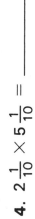

WARM-UP 47

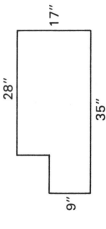

1. $A = L \times W$
   Find A if $L = 1.9$
   $\quad\quad\quad\quad W = .8$

   $A =$ _____

2. $V = L \times W \times H$
   Find V if $L = 1.9$
   $\quad\quad\quad\quad W = .8$
   $\quad\quad\quad\quad H = 10$

   $V =$ _____

3. $P = 2 \times (L + W)$
   Find P if L is $4\frac{1}{2}$
   $\quad\quad\quad\quad W$ is $3\frac{1}{2}$

   $P =$ _____

4. $P = (2 \times L) + (2 \times W)$
   Find P if L is $4\frac{1}{2}$
   $\quad\quad\quad\quad W$ is $3\frac{1}{2}$

   $P =$ _____

5. Find the average of the measurements 2.9 cm, 3.7 cm, 4.6 cm, 5.1 cm, and 6.2 cm.

   _____

BONUS: A boy has 8 pints of water in an 8-pint jar. Another boy has an empty 3-pint jar and an empty 5-pint jar. None of the jars has measurement markings on it. Show how they can divide up the water so that each boy has exactly 4 pints.

26

WARM-UP 49

1. .9 × 3.14 = _____

2. 1.6)‾6.4‾   **3.** .16)‾.64‾

4. How many $\frac{1}{2}$ inches are
in $5\frac{1}{2}$ inches? _____

5. $5\frac{1}{2} \div \frac{1}{2}$ = _____

BONUS:

```
                   ☐  ☐  3
              ×       2  ☐
         ☐  ☐    ☐  1  ☐  7
   ☐  1  4  ☐    7  ☐
☐  2  5,  ☐  ☐    ☐
```

WARM-UP 50

1. .17 × .012 = _____

2. Ms. Mendez bought $3\frac{1}{2}$
pounds of meat at $1.89 per
pound. What did this cost her? _____

3. About how many kilometers is it from
Mudville to Milltown? _____

Scale: 1 cm = 20 km

Mudville •————————————• Milltown

4. (Do this one mentally.) A
backpack costs $48.98. How
much change will there be

from $100? _____

5. (Do this one mentally.)
Groceries cost $13.21. How
much change will there be

from $20? _____

BONUS: What number divided
by 2, 3, 4, or 6 gives a remainder
of 1, but when divided by 7

gives no remainder? _____

WARM-UP 52

1. Make a sketch of a rectangle whose length is approximately twice as long as its width.

2. Make a sketch of a square whose area is approximately 4 square centimeters.

3. This is a sketch of a cubic centimeter. Make a sketch of a cubic inch.

4. 5 weeks 6 days
   + 4 weeks 5 days
   _____
   (Give the answer in lowest terms.)

5. 3 pounds 8 ounces
   − 2 pounds 15 ounces
   _____

BONUS: Spend-Less is having a sale on pencils.

4 short pencils for 10 cents
2 medium pencils for 10 cents
1 long pencil for 10 cents
What 20 pencils can Nancy buy for $1.00?

WARM-UP 51

1. Mark works as a cashier. Show how he can make change for a dollar. Use the fewest number of coins.

Purchase	1¢	5¢	10¢	25¢	50¢
54¢	1		2	1	
68¢					
39¢					
11¢					

2. $(3.9 + 2.7) − (4.6 + 1.5) =$ _____

3. $\$2\frac{1}{2} + \$3.79 + \$5\frac{3}{4} =$ _____

4. Cupcakes are $1.68 per dozen. How much will 14 cost? _____

5. Cat food is on sale at 2 cans for 71¢. How much will a case of 24 cans cost? _____

BONUS: Suppose you snap your fingers once after one minute has elapsed. Now, you wait for 2 minutes and snap your fingers again, and once again after 4 minutes, once again after 8 minutes, etc., etc. .... How many times will you have snapped your fingers at the end of 30 days? _____

28

WARM-UP 54

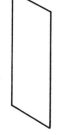

1. The scale on a map is 1" to 300 miles. What distance would $3\frac{1}{2}$" represent? _____

2. Wayne averages 30.4 miles on each gallon of gasoline. At this rate how far can he go on 8.5 gallons? _____

3. Sally earns $7.80 per hour. How much will she earn in $7\frac{1}{2}$ hours? _____

4. Parallel lines never meet. Draw two lines that are parallel to each other.

5. This is a parallelogram. Draw a parallelogram that is skinnier than this one.

BONUS: A man obtained $\frac{1}{8}$ of a dollar from one person, $\frac{1}{6}$ from another, $\frac{1}{5}$ from another, and $\frac{2}{15}$ from another. How much did he get from all? _____

WARM-UP 53

1. Show how to make change for $5.

Purchase	1¢	5¢	10¢	25¢	50¢	$1
$2.40						
$3.12						
$ .34						

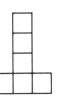

2. $3\frac{4}{5} + 2\frac{1}{2} =$ _____

3. $13 - 5\frac{5}{8} =$ _____

4. $2\frac{1}{2} \times 3\frac{1}{3} =$ _____

5. $15 \div \frac{1}{2} =$ _____

BONUS: Each of these patterns can be folded to make a cube.

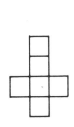

Draw four more patterns that can be folded to make a cube.

29

WARM-UP 56

1. Pencils sell for $1.80 per dozen. How much will 15 pencils cost? _____

2. $.15 \times \boxed{} = .471$

3. $4.18 - \boxed{} = 2.9$

4. 50% of this circle is shaded.

   Shade 25% of this circle.

5. Shade approximately 75% of this rectangle.

BONUS: Imagine a 3-inch cube painted red all over. Now suppose that the cube is cut into 1-inch cubes.

a) How many of the 1-inch cubes will *not* be painted? _____

b) How many will have paint on exactly

   3 faces? _____

   2 faces? _____

   1 face? _____

WARM-UP 55

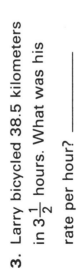

1. $18 \times \boxed{} = 522$

2. $.129 + \boxed{} = 3$

3. Larry bicycled 38.5 kilometers in $3\frac{1}{2}$ hours. What was his rate per hour? _____

4. Perpendicular lines form square corners. These two lines are perpendicular. Draw another pair of perpendicular lines.

5. A right triangle is one in which two of its sides are perpendicular. Draw a right triangle.

BONUS: A family of 4 is having their picture taken. In how many ways can they line up for the photograph? _____

30

WARM-UP 58

1.
$$1 . 9$$
$$15 \overline{\smash{)}\square\square . \square}$$

2. $(\square . \square)^2 = 23.04$

3. $\square + 2.91 = 6.2$

4. Find the average of $3\frac{3}{4}$, $2\frac{1}{8}$, and $3\frac{1}{8}$. _____

5. A square garden is $17\frac{1}{2}$ feet on a side. How much fence is needed to enclose the garden?

   _____

BONUS: Six is called a perfect number; the sum of its divisors is the number itself. (The divisors are 1, 2, and 3; $1 + 2 + 3 = 6$.) There is only one other perfect number less than 30. See if you can find it. _____

WARM-UP 57

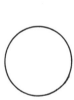

1. Shade 100% of this circle.

2. Shade approximately 90% of this rectangle.

3. Shade approximately 90% of this rectangle.

4. A trapezoid has 4 sides. A trapezoid always has exactly two parallel sides. Draw a trapezoid.

5. A rhombus has four equal sides. Draw a rhombus. Does it have to be a square? _____

BONUS: Use the digits 0 through 9. Make the smallest answer you can that is less than 300.

$$\square\square\square\square\square$$
$$-\ \square\square\square\square$$

31

WARM-UP 59

1. Use the number line. Show the approximate location of 50%, 25%, and 75%.

   0 ⊢————————————⊣ 100%

2. Use the new number line below. Now show the approximate location of 50%, 25%, and 75%.

   0 ⊢————————————⊣ 100%

3. Circle the numbers that are the same as 50%.

   $\frac{1}{2}$, 5%, .5, 5, $\frac{5}{10}$, .50

4. Arrange from smallest to largest.

   50%, .9, $\frac{5}{4}$, 5%

   _____

5. Arrange from smallest to largest.

   .50, 100%, $\frac{3}{2}$, 90%

   _____

BONUS: Carlos has some pennies, nickels, and quarters in his pocket. He has 2 more nickels than quarters. He has twice as many pennies as nickels. The total value is $1.74. How many of each coin does Carlos have?

_____

WARM-UP 60

1. Find the average of these test scores.

   90%, 95%, 100%, 75%   _____

2. An equilateral triangle is one with all sides equal. Sketch an equilateral triangle.

3. Sketch a triangle with exactly two sides equal. This is called an isosceles triangle.

4. Four pounds of bananas cost $1.60. How much will 10 pounds

   cost?   _____

5. Big Spender bought a TV for $398 and a stereo for $389. He gave the clerk $1000. How much change did he get?

   _____

BONUS: If Ross gives me 2 pennies, I will have 3 times as many as he. If I give Ross 3 pennies, we will have the same number.

a) How many pennies does Ross have?

   _____

b) How many pennies do I have?   _____

WARM-UP 61

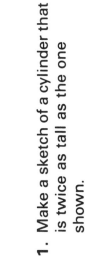

1. $V = L \times W \times H$

Find V if $L = \frac{2}{3}$

$W = \frac{3}{4}$

$H = \frac{4}{5}$

V _____

2. $A = \frac{1}{2} \times B \times H$

Find A if $B = 5.5$

$H = 10$

A _____

3. $(3\frac{1}{2} \times 4) + (2\frac{1}{2} \times 4) =$ _____

4. $(3\frac{1}{2} + 2\frac{1}{2}) \times 4 =$ _____

5. An archaeologist claims to have found a coin that was dated 46 B.C. Do you think he really did?

Explain. _____

_____

BONUS: A number of girls are standing in a circle. They are evenly spaced and are numbered beginning with 1. Number 5 is opposite Number 16.

How many girls are in the circle? _____

WARM-UP 62

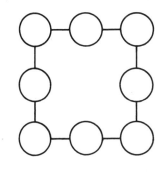

1. Make a sketch of a cylinder that is twice as tall as the one shown.

2. Make a sketch of a cone that is twice as tall as the one shown.

3. Which is longer. . . .
100% of a yard or

10% of a mile? _____

4. Which is longer . . . .
50% of a meter or

90% of a yard? _____

5. This is 25% of a square.
Draw 100% of the square.

BONUS: Use each of the numbers 1 through 8. The sum of the numbers on each side should be 14.

WARM-UP 64

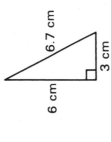

12 cm
8 cm
16 cm
6 cm

6 cm
6.7 cm
3 cm

1. Find the perimeter of this figure. _____

2. Find the area of the figure in problem 1. (The answer is *not* 128 sq cm.) _____

3. Find the perimeter of this right triangle. _____

4. Find the area of the figure in problem 3. _____

5. $1\frac{5}{6} \times \frac{6}{11} =$ _____

BONUS: Six talkative teenagers want their own private telephone system. The system would connect each of their houses with the others.

a) How many wires are needed? _____

b) Suppose another person joined their group. Now, how many wires would be needed? _____

WARM-UP 63

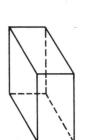

1. Make a sketch of a rectangular solid that is larger than the one shown.

2. A cube is a special kind of rectangular solid. Make a sketch of a cube that is approximately 2 cm on each side.

3. Find the average of Mary's test scores. 75%, 100%, 100%, 81%, 79% _____

4. Julie made 5 baskets out of 10 tries. What percent is this? _____

5. $234{,}234 \div 13 =$ _____ (There is no remainder.)

BONUS: The picture shows seven connected stamps. Show how 3 connected stamps can be torn off. Can you find more than 9 ways?

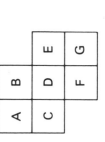

A	B	
C	D	E
	F	G

34

WARM-UP 65

1. $2.5 \times 10 \times 4 \times 5.6 \times 0 \times 6.2 =$ _____

2. $\dfrac{2}{11} + \dfrac{4}{7} + 3 + \dfrac{3}{7} + \dfrac{9}{11} + 7 + \dfrac{1}{3} =$ _____

3. $5 \, \overline{)\, 3 \text{ weeks } 4 \text{ days}}$

4. Four runners ran a 1600-meter relay in 3 min 10 sec. What was the average time per runner? _____

5. Round
   a) 38.219 to the nearest hundredth. _____
   b) 999.99 to the nearest tenth. _____

BONUS: Use only the numbers 1 through 7. The sum in each direction must be the same.

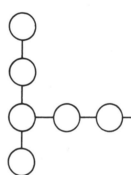

WARM-UP 66

1. What is the approximate length of segment AB in centimeters? _____

A _____ B

2. What is the approximate length of AB in millimeters? _____

3. An example of a right angle is shown. When will the hands of a clock be at right angles to one another? (Give two different times.) _____

4. Draw a 4-sided figure with all right angles. What is the name of your figure? _____

5. What is the square root of 50? Give the answer to the nearest tenth. _____

BONUS: There are 24 players on a baseball squad. 10 of the players can pitch, 6 can play first base, and 4 of the players can do both. How many players can neither pitch nor play first base? _____

WARM-UP 67

1. $5\frac{1}{8} + 3\frac{5}{6} =$ _____

2. $4\frac{1}{10} - 2\frac{7}{10} =$ _____

3. Check your answer to problem 2 by using decimals. _____

4. Change $1\frac{15}{20}$ to a decimal. _____

5. Complete the pattern.
   $1.39, \$1.29, \$1.19, \$1.09, ____, ____,$

BONUS: Mary is having a birthday party. Her mother brings a dish with 26 pieces of candy and passes it around to all the children. Each child takes a piece of candy, in turn, until the plate is empty. Mary gets the first piece. She also gets the next-to-last piece. How many children could be at the party for this to be possible? _____

WARM-UP 68

1. Complete the pattern.
   1.5, 2.4, 3.3, 4.2, ____ , ____ , ____

2. Complete the pattern.
   $1\frac{2}{5}$, $2\frac{4}{5}$, $4\frac{1}{5}$, $5\frac{3}{5}$, ____ , ____ , ____

3. The scale on a map is 1 cm to 40 km. How long a line would you draw to represent a distance of 300 km? _____

4. Find the perimeter of this trapezoid. _____

   2.2 cm / 5.5 cm / 3.8 cm / 10.5 cm

5. $15.01 - \$14.97 =$ _____

BONUS:

$$\square\square \overline{\smash{)}\,4101} \quad 7$$

3 9 □

□□□ □□
□□□ □□

□ □

WARM-UP 70

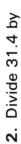

1. Multiply 2.76 by
   a) 10 _____
   b) 100 _____
   c) 1000 _____

2. Divide 31.4 by
   a) 10 _____
   b) 100 _____
   c) 1000 _____

3. Complete the pattern.
   $1\frac{1}{4}$, $2\frac{1}{2}$, $3\frac{3}{4}$, 5, _____, _____, _____,

4. Complete the pattern.
   1.44, 1.32, 1.2, 1.08, _____, _____,

5. Arrange from smallest to largest.
   $\frac{1}{4}$, 24%, 1, $\frac{1}{2}$, .8, $\frac{3}{4}$

BONUS: The answer to an addition problem is 1000. Exactly eight 8's are used in the problem. Show how this is

possible. _____

WARM-UP 69

1. Complete the table showing $.59 hot dogs.

Number	1	2	5	10
Cost $	.59			

2. Records are on sale at $2.99 each. How many can Janet buy

   for $25? _____

3. Soup is on sale at 4 cans for 87¢. How much would you be

   charged for 5 cans? _____

4. $1.7 + 2.9 + \boxed{} = 10$

5. A dog weighs 30 pounds when standing on 4 legs. How much will he weigh when standing on

   3 legs? _____

BONUS: Dead Eye Ernie is in a slump. He's only made 5 out of 21 free throws. How many in a row does he have to make to raise his

record to 50%? _____

to 75%? _____

37

TEACHER'S COMMENTARY

A note about the Bonus problems: In many cases, more than one answer is possible. Please check student answers carefully, since students may find solutions other than those listed here and still be correct.

WARM-UP 1

1. $30.61   *Remind students that $14 is $14.00 not $.14.*

2. $29.85   *This problem can be done mentally by multiplying $2 by 15 and subtracting 15¢ from the result.*

3. $7.81

4. $12.19

5. 292 cm

Bonus:

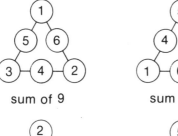

sum of 9   sum of 10

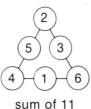   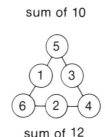

sum of 11   sum of 12

WARM-UP 2

1. 2210

2. 2210   *The answers to problems 1 and 2 are the same due to the distributive property. Hopefully, students will recognize this and apply the property to similar problems occurring later.*

3. $11.99   *The problem can be done mentally if one notes that the difference is just one penny less than $12— ($29 − $17).*

4. 26,645   *Point out the repetition of the digits 385. A six-digit number formed by repeating three digits is always divisible by 13 and by 11 and 7.*

5. 151,495

Bonus: One possible answer:

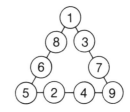

WARM-UP 3

1. 0   *Point out that multiplication by 0 always results in zero.*

2. $2495   *This problem can be done mentally by multiplying $500 by 5 and subtracting $5 from the result.*

3. 2187

4. 2187   *Problems 3 and 4 show the distributive property.*

5. 712 cm

Bonus:
  10 different
  scores

	50	25	10	Total
	✓✓✓			150
	✓✓	✓		125
	✓✓		✓	110
	✓	✓✓		100
	✓	✓	✓	85
	✓		✓✓	70
		✓✓✓		75
		✓✓	✓	60
		✓	✓✓	45
			✓✓✓	30

WARM-UP 4

1. $78.21   *Emphasize that $79 is $79.00.*
2. $18.00
3. $53.20
4. 16,632   *Point out the repetition of the digits 216.*
5. 42   *Remind students that the average must be between 32 and 51, the lowest and highest numbers.*

Bonus: 16 triangles   *One approach to solving this problem is to select a corner along the outside of the main triangle and then find all the smaller triangles having the same corner. Repeat the process with the other corners.*

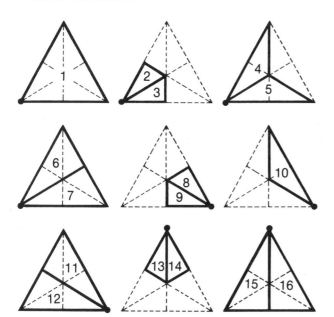

WARM-UP 5

1. 174 cm
2. $2.64
3. 71   *Remind students that multiplication by 0 always results in zero.*
4. 415
5. $57.21   *Relate this problem to the amount of change given from $100 when two gifts are purchased.*

Bonus: 24 triangles   *This problem can be solved using the method shown for BONUS 4. (Be sure to also include the corners of the center triangle.)*

WARM-UP 6

1. 35
2. $6400   *Ask the question "Which is the number closer to—$6400 or $6500?"*
3. 56,000
4. $22.20
5. $22.20   *Problems 4 and 5 show the distributive property.*

Bonus:

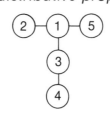

sum of 8

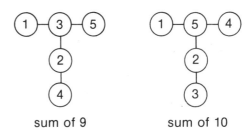

sum of 9   sum of 10

WARM-UP 7

1. 999,999 *Emphasize place value.*
2. 718 *Emphasize shortcuts. The problem can be done mentally by rearranging the numbers to form hundreds—(95 + 5) + (88 + 12) + (25 + 75) + 410 + 8.*
3. 157
4.

Number	1	2	4	8	16
Cost	.85	1.70	3.40	6.80	13.60

Emphasize looking for patterns—as the number doubles, so does the price.

5. 6 cm

Bonus:

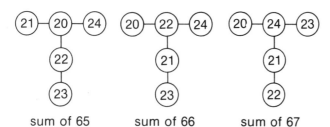

sum of 65   sum of 66   sum of 67

WARM-UP 8

1. 12
2. 17
3. 667
4. 26,299 *Point out the repetition of the digits 289.*
5. Yes, but it's not a holiday.

Bonus: 28 ducks and 4 cows

WARM-UP 9

1. 741 R 3
2. 349 *This problem can be done mentally by rearranging the numbers to form hundreds— (89 + 11) + (70 + 30) + (15 + 85) + 49.*

3. 25
4. 10 cm
5. 100 mm

Bonus: 80 goats and 20 chickens

WARM-UP 10

1. 999,999,999
2.

Number	1	2	3	4	8	16
Cost	.45	.90	1.35	1.80	3.60	7.20

3. 64, 128, 256, 512
4. 42, 50, 58, 66
5. 21, 28, 36, 45 *This pattern is often called the Triangular Number Pattern.*

Bonus: 18 rectangles *One approach to solving this problem is to select two corners of a rectangle and find all the rectangles having the same two corners.*

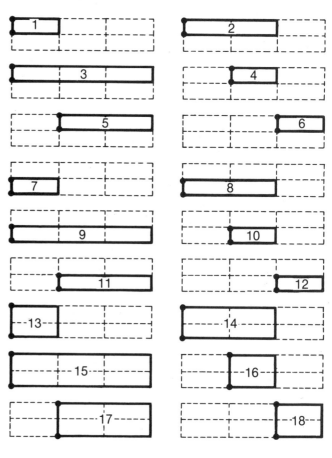

40

WARM-UP 11

1. a) 7 cm   b) 70 mm
2. a) 41, 33, 25, 17   b) 27, 35, 44, 54
3. 65   *Remind students that the multiplication must be done first.*
4. 2346
5. 109,824 *Point out the repetition of the digits 76.*

Bonus: 30 rectangles   *This problem can be solved using the method shown for BONUS 10.*

WARM-UP 12

1. 74 × 65 = 4810
2. $33.84 *Remind students that $17 is $17.00.*
3. 541 R 10
4. 234 sq in.   *Reinforce the concept of area.*
5. 901 sq cm

Bonus: Two possible answers:

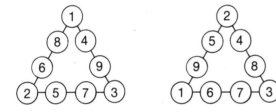

WARM-UP 13

1. $8.47
2. $15.62
3. 100 cm
4. 525 sq cm
5. 135   *Remind students that the multiplication must be done first.*

Bonus: One possible answer:

2	7	6
9	5	1
4	3	8

WARM-UP 14

1. a) 234,000   b) 1,000,000
   c) 98,765,000
2. 69   *Show the students how this formula can be used to find the perimeter of a triangle.*
3. 200   *Show the students how this formula can be used to find the perimeter of a rectangle.*
4. a) $150   b) $100
5. 19,747 *Point out the repetition of the digits 217.*

Bonus: One possible answer:

5	10	3
4	6	8
9	2	7

WARM-UP 15

1. $23.18   *The problem can be done mentally—$99.99 is one cent less than $100.*
2. 999,999,999,999
3. $492.19
4. 104
5. 104   *The formulas in problems 4 and 5 both can be used to find the perimeter of a rectangle. Use these problems to reinforce the distributive property.*

Bonus: The result is the same as the 3-digit number you start with.

WARM-UP 16

1. 210   *Here's an easy way to find the sum of the first 20 consecutive numbers (1 + 2 + 3 + ... + 19 + 20). Add the first and last, the second and second to last, etc. Each sum is 21, and there are 10 of these. 21 × 10 = 210.*

2. a) 560   b) 5600   c) 56,000

3. 120 cu in.   *Reinforce the concept of volume.*

4. 300 cu cm

5. 49, 64, 81, 100, 121   *This pattern is often called the Square Number Pattern.*

Bonus: a) 7, 8, 15, <u>23</u>, <u>38</u>, <u>61</u>, <u>99</u>, <u>160</u>
b) 6, <u>3</u>, 9, <u>12</u>, <u>21</u>, <u>33</u>, <u>54</u>, <u>87</u>
c) 2, <u>10</u>, <u>12</u>, 22, 34, <u>56</u>, <u>90</u>

WARM-UP 17

1. 820   *Suggest to the students that they use the method discussed in Warm-Up 16 (1 + 40, 2 + 39,...). 41 × 20 = 820.*

2. 87

3. $1.16

4. 20¢

5. 3375 cu mm

Bonus: a) 10, 3, 13, 16, <u>29</u>, <u>45</u>, <u>74</u>, <u>119</u>, <u>193</u>
b) 1, <u>4</u>, <u>5</u>, <u>9</u>, 14, <u>23</u>, <u>37</u>, <u>60</u>, 97

WARM-UP 18

1. 125

2. 216

3. $3.71

4. 9   *This is a trick question.*

5. 1850   *This problem can be done mentally by rearranging the numbers—(988 + 12) + (297 + 3) + 550.*

Bonus: a) 5, 12, 17, 29, <u>46</u>, <u>75</u>, <u>121</u>, <u>196</u>
b) <u>3</u>, <u>4</u>, <u>7</u>, <u>11</u>, <u>18</u>, 29, 47
c) 3, $3\frac{1}{2}$, $6\frac{1}{2}$, 10, $16\frac{1}{2}$, $26\frac{1}{2}$

WARM-UP 19

1. 5050   *Suggest that students use the method discussed in Warm-Up 16.*

2. 729   *Emphasize that 9^3 is not the same as 9 × 3.*

3. $1.55

4. 610

5. 4908

Bonus:

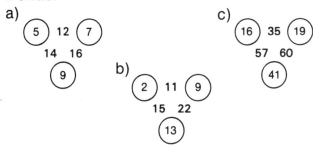

WARM-UP 20

1. 16

2. $3588   *The problem can be done mentally—(12 × $300) − $12.*

3. $98.01   *The problem can be done mentally by subtracting one dollar and adding one penny.*

4. a) $190   b) $186

5. 0   *There is no dirt in a hole.*

Bonus:

a)
```
   7   27   20
     37   50
        30
```
b)
```
   2   17   15
     31   44
        29
```
c)
```
  10½   19   8½
     14   12
        3½
```

42

WARM-UP 21

1. 7   *Emphasize that 2^5 is not the same as 5^2.*

2. 14¢

3. 154 R 4

4. $26.28

5. 20.43   *Compare this problem to problem 4. Tell the students to think of the numbers as dollars and cents.*

Bonus: 27 triangles   *This problem can be solved using the method shown for BONUS 4.*

Bonus: Some possible answers: $1 = \frac{4+4}{4+4}$

$$2 = \frac{4}{4} + \frac{4}{4}$$
$$3 = (4 + 4 + 4) \div 4$$
$$4 = \frac{4-4}{4} + 4$$
$$5 = (4 \times 4 + 4) \div 4$$
$$6 = \frac{4+4}{4} + 4$$
$$7 = 4 + 4 - \frac{4}{4}$$
$$8 = 4 + 4 + 4 - 4$$
$$9 = 4 + 4 + \frac{4}{4}$$
$$10 = \frac{4}{.4} + 4 - 4$$

WARM-UP 22

1. See student's drawing.

2. See student's drawing.

3. $.41   *This problem can be done mentally— ($1.00 − .60) + .01.*

4. $.15

5. 313   *Emphasize the method for checking a division problem— multiply the divisor by the quotient and add the remainder.*

Bonus: 36 rectangles   *This problem can be solved using the method shown for BONUS 10.*

WARM-UP 23

1. $15.75

2. 226.77   *Compare this problem to problem 1. Tell the students to think of the numbers as dollars and cents.*

3. See student's drawing.

4. See student's drawing.

5. Some possible answers:

$$\frac{2}{4}, \frac{3}{6}, \frac{4}{8}, \frac{5}{10}, \frac{10}{20}, \frac{17}{34}, \frac{24}{48}, \frac{50}{100}$$

WARM-UP 24

1. 21 cm   *The problem can be done mentally.*

2. 1191   *Emphasize the method for checking a division problem— multiply the divisor by the quotient.*

3. 1, 2, 3, 4, 6, 8, 12, 16, 24, 48

4. a) 74   b) 740

5. a) 74   b) 740

Bonus: Impossible.   *Point out that the sum of any three odd numbers is always odd. The sum of any four odd numbers is always even.*

WARM-UP 25

1. Each part is $\frac{1}{6}$.

2. 19.5

3. $15.21

4. 11.38   *Compare this problem to problem 3. Tell the students to think of the numbers as dollars and cents.*

5. See student's drawing.

Bonus:
$$\begin{array}{r} 523 \\ -476 \\ \hline 47 \end{array}$$

WARM-UP 26

1. Some possible answers:
$\frac{2}{6}$, $\frac{3}{9}$, $\frac{4}{12}$, $\frac{5}{15}$, $\frac{10}{30}$, $\frac{25}{75}$

2. a) 32.4   b) 324   c) 3240

3. 14 cm   *The problem can be done mentally.*

4. Either about 14 cm $\times$ 21.5 cm *or* about 21.5 cm $\times$ 28 cm

5. $5.00   *The problem can be done mentally. Find the cost of $\frac{1}{3}$ of the pizza and multiply this result by 2.*

Bonus: Two possible answers:

$$\begin{array}{r} 786 \\ +249 \\ \hline 1035 \end{array} \qquad \begin{array}{r} 724 \\ +365 \\ \hline 1089 \end{array}$$

WARM-UP 27

1. 2.08

2. a) $18.95   *The problem can be done mentally—($38 − 19) − .05.*
   b) 16.63   *The problem can be done mentally—(42 − 26) + .63.*

3. See student's drawing

4. Some possible answers: $\frac{1}{3}$, $\frac{3}{8}$, $\frac{5}{12}$

5. 361

Bonus: One possible answer:

$$6 - \frac{22 + 7 + 1}{6} = 1$$

WARM-UP 28

1. See student's drawing

2. Some possible answers: .2, .3, .4, .17, .34

3. 48   *Emphasize mental computation.*

4. 60   *Emphasize mental computation.*

5. One nickel and one half-dollar. *This is a trick question.*

Bonus: 12 ways

d	n	p
2	1	0
2	0	5
1	3	0
1	2	5
1	1	10
1	0	15
0	5	0
0	4	5
0	3	10
0	2	15
0	1	20
0	0	25

WARM-UP 29

1. $52.64

2. $52.64   *Problems 1 and 2 show the distributive property.*

3. 1, $1\frac{1}{4}$, $1\frac{1}{2}$, $1\frac{3}{4}$

4. 1, 1.25, 1.50, 1.75   *This problem is the decimal form of problem 3.*

5. $\frac{1}{2}$, .5 , $\frac{5}{10}$, .50

Bonus: Two possible answers—four 5s, one 23, one 31; two 5s, three 11s, one 31

WARM-UP 30

1. Some possible answers: .33, .34, .35, .339

2. Some possible answers:
$\frac{5}{8}$, $\frac{6}{8}$, $\frac{7}{8}$, $\frac{9}{10}$, $\frac{15}{24}$

3. 15 sq cm

4. a) 1, 2, 3, 4, 6, 9, 12, 18, 36   b) 1, 53
Note that 53 is a prime number.

5. 5¢   *This is a trick question. Many students will give an answer of one dime. (The pen costs $1.05.)*

Bonus: a) 1 quarter, 2 dimes, 3 pennies
b) 2 dimes, 4 nickels, 8 pennies

WARM-UP 31

1. 23   *Emphasize the shortcut of rearranging the numbers —*

$$(1\tfrac{9}{10} + \tfrac{1}{10}) + (5\tfrac{1}{2} + 5\tfrac{1}{2}) + 10.$$

2. 23   *Point out that problem 2 is the decimal form of problem 1.*

3. $1\tfrac{3}{8}$, $1\tfrac{5}{8}$, $1\tfrac{7}{8}$, $2\tfrac{1}{8}$

4. a) $350.00   b) $346.00   c) $345.70

5. a) 530.00   b) 529.00   c) 529.50
Point out that in problems 4 and 5, "nearest $10" and "nearest tens," etc. refer to the same place value.

Bonus: 18 ways

q	d	n	p
1	0	1	0
1	0	0	5
0	3	0	0
0	2	2	0
0	2	1	5
0	2	0	10
0	1	4	0
0	1	3	5
0	1	2	10
0	1	1	15
0	1	0	20
0	0	6	0
0	0	5	5
0	0	4	10
0	0	3	15
0	0	2	20
0	0	1	25
0	0	0	30

WARM-UP 32

1. $\tfrac{1}{100}$, $\tfrac{1}{4}$, $\tfrac{1}{2}$, $\tfrac{9}{10}$

2. .01, .25, .5, .9   *Point out that problems 1 and 2 list the same numbers in fraction and decimal forms.*

3. 18 cm   *Point out that .5 and $\tfrac{1}{2}$ name the same number. Emphasize mental computation.*

4. a) $71.64   b) 43.44

5. Impossible.   *This problem can lead to some good discussion— 0.999. . . . never quite reaches 1.0.*

Bonus: 12 children

WARM-UP 33

1. a) 31.41   b) 416   c) 100

2. 62 cm   a) 15.5 + 15.5 + 15.5 + 15.5   b) 15.5 × 4

3. 122 in.

4. $4.01   *Emphasize mental computation.*

5. 12,111

Bonus: 30 squares   *This problem can be solved using the method shown for BONUS 10.*

WARM-UP 34

1. Some possible answers: $\tfrac{4}{6}$, $\tfrac{8}{12}$, $\tfrac{12}{18}$, $\tfrac{16}{24}$

2. Some possible answers: $\tfrac{2}{8}$, $\tfrac{3}{12}$, $\tfrac{4}{16}$, $\tfrac{5}{20}$

3. Some possible answers: $\tfrac{4}{12}$, $\tfrac{5}{12}$, $\tfrac{6}{12}$, $\tfrac{7}{12}$

4. $\tfrac{11}{12}$

5. $\tfrac{5}{12}$ *Point out that problems 3, 4, and 5 are related to problems 1 and 2. Emphasize that in order to add or subtract unlike fractions, one has to find equivalent fractions with a common denominator.*

Bonus:

$$
\begin{array}{r}
982 \\
\times\ 306 \\
\hline
5892 \\
000 \\
2946 \\
\hline
300{,}492 \\
\end{array}
$$

WARM-UP 35

1. 15 min
2. 8 hr
3. 11 ft 4 in.
4. 2 yd 2 ft
5. 8 cm 4 mm   *Emphasize that the metric system is a decimal system; computation is easier with decimals.*

Bonus: 28 games

	1	2	3	4	5	6	7	8
1		✔	✔	✔	✔	✔	✔	✔
2			✔	✔	✔	✔	✔	✔
3				✔	✔	✔	✔	✔
4					✔	✔	✔	✔
5						✔	✔	✔
6							✔	✔
7								✔
8								

WARM-UP 36

1. 16 ft   *Emphasize mental computation. The problem is easy if the length and width are first added together.*

2. 1 yd 1 ft
3. $1\frac{1}{12}$
4. $\frac{85}{100} = \frac{17}{20}$
5. $\frac{48}{100} = \frac{12}{25}$

Bonus:

$$
\begin{array}{r}
24 \\
214\overline{)5136} \\
428 \\
\hline
856 \\
856 \\
\hline
0
\end{array}
$$

WARM-UP 37

1. .001, $\frac{1}{4}$, .50, $\frac{2}{3}$, .8

2. $\frac{40}{30}$, $1\frac{1}{3}$, $1.3\bar{3}$, $\frac{8}{6}$
   Review the meaning of $1.3\bar{3}$ (repeating decimal).

3. $3\frac{2}{8}$, $\frac{13}{4}$, 3.25, $2\frac{5}{4}$

4. $1\frac{7}{12}$

5. $\frac{3}{10}$

Bonus: a) 3 nickels, 2 pennies
   b) 2 nickels, 3 pennies
   c) 2 quarters, 3 pennies
   d) 3 dimes, 2 nickels
   e) 4 dimes, 1 penny
   f) 2 quarters, 1 dime,
      1 nickel, 1 penny
      or
      1 half-dollar,
      3 nickels, 1 penny

WARM-UP 38

1. 1 yd 1 ft 7 in.
2. 18
3. 5.8   *Emphasize the importance of the guess and check procedure.*
4. 1.0, .7, .4
5. 39.96

Bonus: 32,768; not possible

WARM-UP 39

1. 1.11   *Remind the students to place a zero after the 5 in 1.5 before trying to subtract.*

2. 8.17

3. 2.06   *Remind students to write all the numbers in the same form—fraction or decimal. In this case, decimal is easier.*

4. 1.50

5. $1\frac{1}{2}$ *Point out that problems 4 and 5 are the same numbers in different forms.*

Bonus: 155 pounds

WARM-UP 40

1. $4\frac{5}{8}$ "

2. 3.24 sq cm

3. 12 cm *Emphasize that this is an application of square root.*

4. 5.5 *Emphasize the estimation, and guess and check problem solving techniques.*

5. 88.888

Bonus: 45 handshakes

	1	2	3	4	5	6	7	8	9	10
1		✔	✔	✔	✔	✔	✔	✔	✔	✔
2			✔	✔	✔	✔	✔	✔	✔	✔
3				✔	✔	✔	✔	✔	✔	✔
4					✔	✔	✔	✔	✔	✔
5						✔	✔	✔	✔	✔
6							✔	✔	✔	✔
7								✔	✔	✔
8									✔	✔
9										✔
10										

WARM-UP 41

1. 82.6

2. 82.6 *Problems 1 and 2 show the distributive property.*

3. 10 cm *Emphasize mental computation.*

4. 5.76 sq cm

5. 12 *This is a trick question. Some students may think the answer is 4.*

Bonus: One possible answer:

6	7	10	11
13	9	4	8
12	16	5	1
3	2	15	14

WARM-UP 42

1. 73

2. 73 *Point out that problems 1 and 2 are similar.*

3. 35

4. 35 *Point out that problems 3 and 4 are similar.*

5. 11

Bonus:

$$
\begin{array}{r}
117 \\
\times\ 319 \\
\hline
1053 \\
117 \\
351 \\
\hline
37{,}323 \\
\end{array}
$$

WARM-UP 43

1. 3.5

2. 2.1

3. $5\frac{1}{4}$

4. $5\frac{1}{4}$ *Point out that problems 3 and 4 are the same.*

5. $9\frac{7}{8}$

Bonus:

WARM-UP 44

1. 3 *Emphasize that this problem can be done mentally by rearranging the numbers— (2.8 + 3.2) + (2.9 + 3.1) + 3.*

2. 5 m

3. 20 cm

4. $2\frac{1}{4}$

5. 5.1

Bonus:

a) 10 committees
12 23 34 45
13 24 35
14 25
15

b) 10 committees
123 234 345
124 235
125 245
134
135
145

WARM-UP 45

1. 27   *Emphasize mental computation by rearranging the numbers— ($5\frac{1}{8} + 1\frac{7}{8}$), etc.*

2. 12.167

3. $6\frac{5}{6}$

4. 27,000 cu cm   *Review the concept of volume.*

5. 12.167   *Point out that this is the same problem as problem 2.*

Bonus: 24 eggs

WARM-UP 46

1. .07, .17, .7, .71, 7

2. 2.079   *Emphasize estimation.*

3. 2.145   *Emphasize estimation.*

4. a) 59.3   b) 593   c) 5930

5. a) 649   b) 64.9   c) 6.49

Bonus: One possible answer:

$$13 + 10 - 8 - \frac{8}{2} = 11$$

WARM-UP 47

1. 1.52   *Point out that this is the formula for finding the area of a rectangle.*

2. 15.2   *Point out that this is the formula for finding the volume of a rectangular solid.*

3. 16

4. 16   *The formulas used in problems 3 and 4 are equivalent.*

5. 4.5 cm

Bonus: One solution uses six steps:

Fill the "5" from the "8."
Fill the "3" from the "5."
Pour the "3" into the "8."
Pour the "5" into the "3."
Fill the "5" from the "8."
Fill the "3" from the "5."

WARM-UP 48

1. 104″

2. $15\frac{3}{4}$

3. 15.75

4. $10\frac{71}{100}$ *Emphasize that the problem is easy to solve by using decimals—2.1 × 5.1.*

5. 10 ft 3 in.

Bonus: One possible answer:

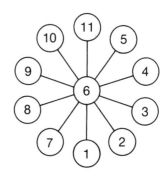

WARM-UP 49

1. 2.826

2. 4

3. 4   *Point out the positions of the decimal points in problems 2 and 3.*

4. 11

5. 11   *Point out that problems 4 and 5 are the same.*

Bonus:
$$
\begin{array}{r}
573 \\
\times\ 219 \\
\hline
5157 \\
573 \\
1146 \\
\hline
125,487
\end{array}
$$

WARM-UP 50

1. .00204

2. $6.62

3. 160 km

4. $51.02   *Emphasize mental computation.*

48

5. $6.79   *Emphasize mental computation.*

Bonus: 49

WARM-UP 51

1.

	1¢	5¢	10¢	25¢	50¢
54¢	1		2	1	
68¢	2	1		1	
39¢	1		1		1
11¢	4		1	1	1

Emphasize "counting" forward to $1.00—(54¢, 55¢, 65¢, 75¢, $1).

2. .5

3. $12.04

4. $1.96   *Explain that students can find the cost of 1, then 14.*

5. $8.52   *Explain that students can find the cost of 24 by multiplying $.71 by 12.*

Bonus: 16 times   1440 min = 1 day
43,200 min = 30 days
1; 2; 4; 8; 16; 32; 64; 128; 256; 512; 1024; 2048; 4096; 8192; 16,384; 32,768

WARM-UP 52

1. See student's drawing.

2. See student's drawing.   *Review the concept of area.*

3. See student's drawing.   *Review the concept of volume.*

4. 10 weeks 4 days

5. 9 ounces

Bonus: Two possible answers:

12 short pencils, 2 medium pencils, and 6 long pencils
            or
8 short pencils, 8 medium pencils, and 4 long pencils

WARM-UP 53

1.

	1¢	5¢	10¢	25¢	50¢	$1
$2.40			1		1	2
$3.12	3		1	1	1	1
$ .34	1	1	1		1	4

Emphasize "counting" forward to $5.00.

2. $6\frac{3}{10}$

3. $7\frac{3}{8}$

4. $8\frac{1}{3}$

5. 30   *Remind students that there are 30 half-dollars in $15.*

Bonus: Nine more patterns are possible:

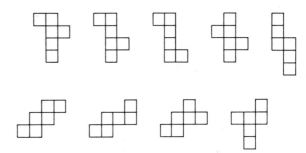

WARM-UP 54

1. 1050 miles   *Emphasize mental computation—(3 × 300) + ($\frac{1}{2}$ × 300).*

2. 258.4 miles   *Point out that students can check to see if their answers make sense by estimating—(30 mi × 8 gal).*

3. $58.50

4. See student's drawing.

5. See student's drawing.

Bonus: $\$\frac{5}{8}$

49

WARM-UP 55

1. 29

2. 2.871

3. 11 km per hr   *Emphasize using estimation to see if the answer seems reasonable—(40 km ÷ 4 hr).*

4. See student's drawing.

5. See student's drawing.

Bonus: 24 ways

1234	2134	3124	4123
1243	2143	3142	4132
1324	2314	3214	4213
1342	2341	3241	4231
1423	2413	3412	4312
1432	2431	3421	4321

WARM-UP 56

1. $2.25

2. 3.14

3. 1.28

4. See student's drawing.

5. See student's drawing.

Bonus: a) 1 cube will not be painted.
  b) 8 cubes will have paint on exactly 3 faces.
     12 cubes will have paint on exactly 2 faces.
     6 cubes will have paint on exactly 1 face.

WARM-UP 57

1. See student's drawing.

2. See student's drawing.

3. See student's drawing.   *Emphasize that the shaded portions in problems 2 and 3 are different since the 100% quantities are different in size.*

4. See student's drawing.

5. See student's drawing; no

Bonus:
$$\begin{array}{r} 50{,}123 \\ -\,49{,}876 \\ \hline 247 \end{array}$$

WARM-UP 58

1. 28.5   *Emphasize the method for checking a division problem—multiply the divisor by the quotient.*

2. 4.8   *Discuss how guess and check can be used to find an answer.*

3. 3.29

4. 3

5. 70 ft   *Remind students that this is an application of perimeter.*

Bonus: 28. It's divisors are 1, 2, 4, 7, and 14.

WARM-UP 59

1. See student's drawing.

2. See student's drawing.   *Emphasize that the respective locations in problems 1 and 2 are different since the 100% lengths are different.*

3. $\frac{1}{2}$, .5, $\frac{5}{10}$, .50

4. 5%, 50%, .9, $\frac{5}{4}$

5. .50, 90%, 100%, $\frac{3}{2}$

Bonus: 5 quarters, 7 nickels, 14 pennies

WARM-UP 60

1. 90%

2. See student's drawing.

3. See student's drawing.

4. $4.00   *Remind students that they can first find the cost of 1 pound, then 10 pounds.*

5. $213

Bonus: a) Ross has 7 pennies.
      b) I have 13 pennies.

WARM-UP 61

1. $\frac{2}{5}$

2. 27.5   *Point out that this formula can be used to find the area of a triangle.*

3. 24

4. 24   *Students should recognize the use of the distributive property in problems 3 and 4.*

5. No, because "B.C." should not be on a coin prior to the time of Christ.

Bonus: 22 girls

WARM-UP 62

1. See student's drawing.

2. See student's drawing.

3. 10% of a mile

4. 90% of a yard   *Problems 3 and 4 can lead to a good discussion about relative sizes.*

5. See student's drawing.

Bonus: One possible answer:

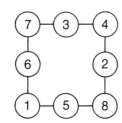

WARM-UP 63

1. See student's drawing.

2. See student's drawing.

3. 87%

4. 50%

5. 18,018   *Note the repetition of the digits 234.*

Bonus: There are 10 ways.

ABC	BCD	DEF	GFE
ABD	BDF	DFG	
ACD	BDE	DEG	

WARM-UP 64

1. 48 cm

2. 120 sq cm

3. 15.7 cm

4. 9 sq cm

5. 1   *Point out that the numbers are reciprocals of each other.*

Bonus: a) 6 teenagers—15 wires
      b) 7 teenagers—21 wires

	1	2	3	4	5	6	7
1		✔	✔	✔	✔	✔	✔
2			✔	✔	✔	✔	✔
3				✔	✔	✔	✔
4					✔	✔	✔
5						✔	✔
6							✔
7							

WARM-UP 65

1. 0   *Remind students of the multiplication property of 0.*

2. $12\frac{1}{3}$ *Emphasize rearrangement of numbers and mental computation.*

3. 5 days

4. 47.5 sec

5. a) 38.22   b) 1000

Bonus: Two possible answers:

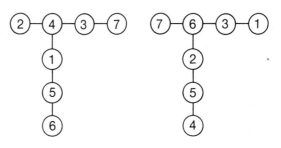

sum of 16   sum of 17

WARM-UP 66

1. 9 cm

2. 90 mm

3. 3:00 and 9:00   *Students might suggest 6:15, etc. However, a right angle is not formed, since the hour hand is slightly past the hour.*

4. Rectangle   *Some students may draw a square. Emphasize that a square is a rectangle.*

5. 7.1

Bonus: 12 Players

$$24 - (6 + 4 + 2) = 12$$

p   fb

WARM-UP 67

1. $8\frac{23}{24}$

2. $1\frac{4}{10}$

3. 1.4   *Emphasize that many problems are easier to work by using decimals.*

4. 1.75

5. $.99, $.89, $.79

Bonus: All the factors of 24: 1, 2, 3, 4, 6, 8, 12, 24

WARM-UP 68

1. 5.1, 6.0, 6.9

2. 7, $8\frac{2}{5}$, $9\frac{4}{5}$

3. 7.5 cm

4. 22 cm   *Emphasize mental computation by rearranging numbers.*

5. $.04   *Emphasize mental computation.*

Bonus: Two possible answers:

```
        71              73
  57 ⟌ 4101       56 ⟌ 4101
       399             392
       ----            ----
       111             181
        57             168
       ----            ----
        54              13
```

WARM-UP 69

1.

Number	1	2	5	10
Cost	.59	1.18	2.95	5.90

2. 8   *Emphasize estimation and mental computation.*

3. $1.09

4. 5.4

5. 30 pounds   *This is a trick question.*

Bonus: 11 in a row to make 50%; 43 in a row to make 75%

WARM-UP 70

1. a) 27.6   b) 276   c) 2760

2. a) 3.14   b) .314   c) .0314

3. $6\frac{1}{4}$, $7\frac{1}{2}$, $8\frac{3}{4}$

4. .96, .84, .72

5. 24%, $\frac{1}{4}$, $\frac{1}{2}$, $\frac{3}{4}$, .8, 1   *Students will no doubt need more practice in arranging a mixture of fractions, decimals, and percents.*

Bonus: 888 + 88 + 8 + 8 + 8